Houghton Mifflin

Reading

Surprises

Senior Authors
J. David Cooper
John J. Pikulski

Authors
David J. Chard
Gilbert Garcia
Claude Goldenberg
Phyllis Hunter
Marjorie Y. Lipson
Shane Templeton
Sheila Valencia
MaryEllen Vogt

Consultants
Linda H. Butler
Linnea C. Ehri
Carla Ford

HOUGHTON MIFFLIN

BOSTON

Cover illustration by B. Jude Reardon.

Acknowledgments begin on page 232.

Printed in the U.S.A.

ISBN: 0-618-61933-X

2 3 4 5 6 7 8 9 10 DOW 11 10 09 08 07 06

Surprises

Home Sweet Home

Home Sweet Home

Realistic Fiction

Focus on Genre

POETRY

Animal Adventures

Animal Adventures

Home Sweet Home

The Very Nicest Place

The fish lives in the brook,
The bird lives in the tree,
But home's the very nicest place
For a little child like me.

Anonymous

Moving Day

Genre   **Fantasy**

A Home in a Shell

The next story you will read is about a crab who has grown too big for its shell. Will the crab find a new home?

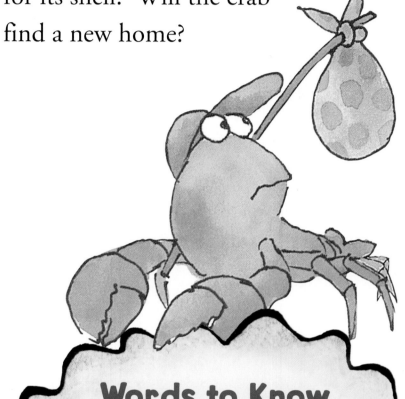

Words to Know

grow	room
light	these
long	this
more	that's
other	smooth
right	why
small	

Practice Sentences

1. There is no more room to grow in this shell.

2. That's why I must find a new shell.

3. This one is too long.

4. This one is too light.

5. This one is too smooth.

6. These other small shells are not right!

7. This shell is the best match.

MOVING DAY

by
ROBERT KALAN

pictures by
YOSSI ABOLAFIA

Strategy Focus

Read Together As you read the story, ask yourself about the kinds of shells the hermit crab finds.

This shell is snug.

This shell is tight.

I will find a shell that's right.

This shell is too big.

This shell is too small.

Too big, too small,
these shells will not do at all.

This shell is too long.

This shell is too wide.

Too long, too wide,
too big, too small,
these shells will not do at all.

This shell is too heavy.

This shell is too light.

28

Too heavy, too light,
too long, too wide,
too big, too small,
these shells will not do at all.

This shell is too rough.

This shell is too smooth.

Too rough, too smooth,
too heavy, too light,
too long, too wide,
too big, too small,
these shells will not do at all.

This shell is too fancy.

This shell is too plain.

Too fancy,

 too plain,

too rough,

 too smooth,

too heavy,

 too light,

too long,

 too wide,

too big,

 too small,

these shells will
not do at all.

This shell is too —

Wait!

It's NOT too snug.
It's NOT too tight.
This shell is the one that's right.

This shell has more room inside.
Room to grow, room to hide.

I know why this shell is fine.
It's like that other shell of mine.

Meet the Author and the Illustrator

Robert Kalan knows a lot about reading. He was once a kindergarten teacher. Today he likes writing animal stories.

Yossi Abolafia drew cartoons for TV. Now he draws comic strips for newspapers. He tries to tell stories with his pictures.

Internet

To find out more about Robert Kalan and Yossi Abolafia, visit Education Place.

www.eduplace.com/kids

43

Responding

Think About the Story

1. Why did it take a long time for the hermit crab to find the right home?

2. What did the crab learn about shells?

3. When will the crab need to find a new home?

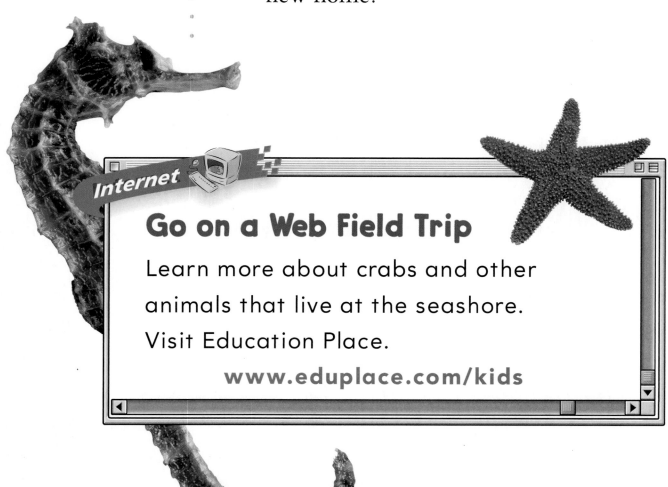

Internet

Go on a Web Field Trip

Learn more about crabs and other animals that live at the seashore. Visit Education Place.

www.eduplace.com/kids

Compare Pictures

Look carefully at the color, shape, and size of each shell in the story. Describe to a partner what each shell looks like.

Informing

Write the Answer to a Question

What did the hermit crab learn by the end of the story? Write a sentence to answer the question.

Tips

- Start your sentence with a capital letter.
- End your sentence with a period.

Science Article

Skill: How to Read a Science Article

- **Read** the title.

- **Look** at the photos.

- **Predict** what you will learn.

- **Ask** questions.

- **Reread** if something is not clear.

Hermit Crabs

What's it like to pull your house on your back? Ask a hermit crab — it would know!

Many crabs have a hard shell, but not the hermit crab. Its back is soft.

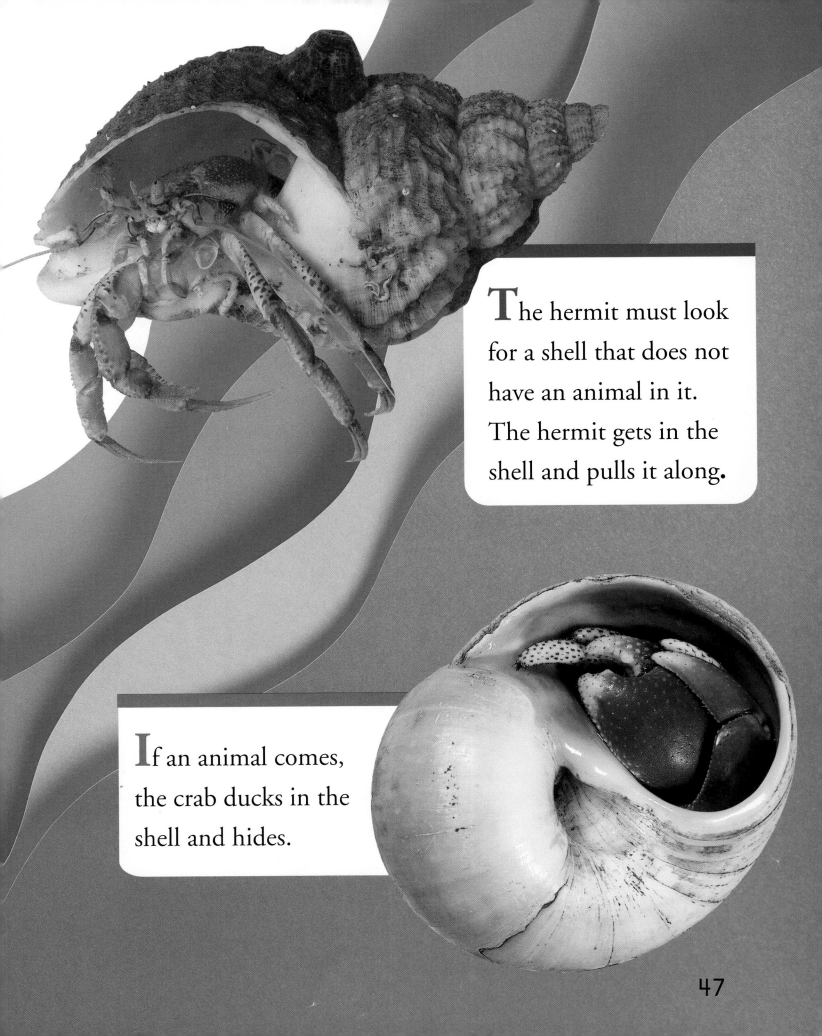

The hermit must look for a shell that does not have an animal in it. The hermit gets in the shell and pulls it along.

If an animal comes, the crab ducks in the shell and hides.

This hermit is much too big for its shell. It must switch shells. Here's a big shell! The hermit pulls out of its first house. Then it pops right in the new one.

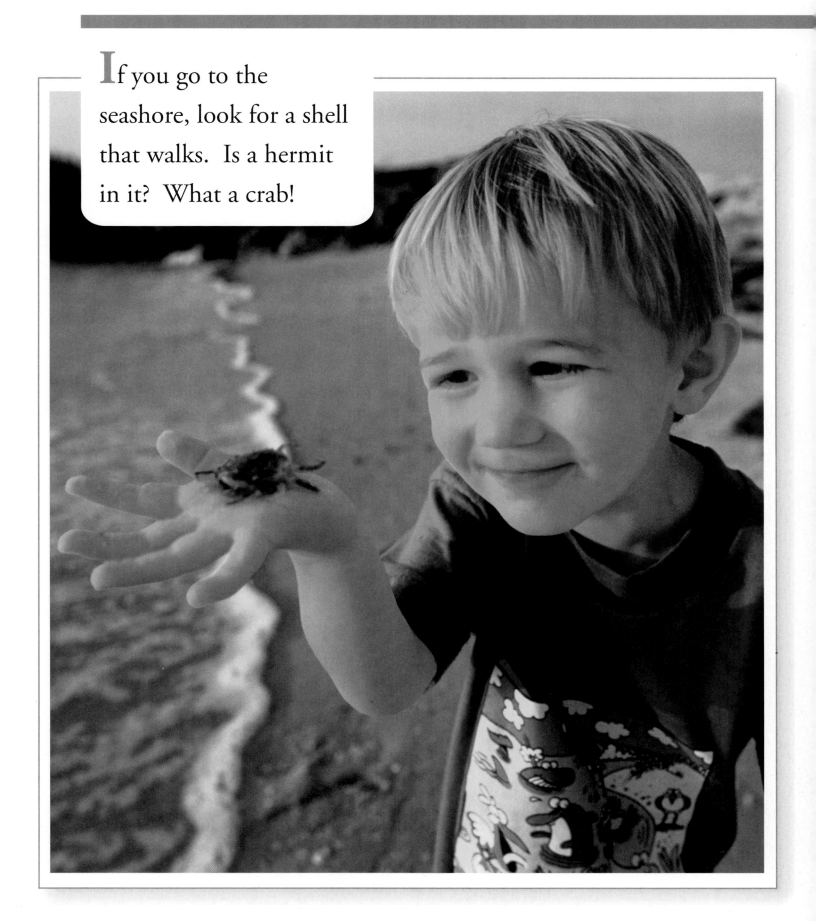

If you go to the seashore, look for a shell that walks. Is a hermit in it? What a crab!

A Personal Narrative

A personal narrative is a true story about something that happened to the writer. Use this student's writing as a model when you write a personal narrative of your own.

A good **beginning** tells what the narrative is about.

Details help the reader picture what happened.

The Lost Turtle

I lost my turtle. His name is Herman. I put up signs all around Jacksonville. So every day I sat by the phone. It was not fun when he was gone.

50

I cried and cried. And then when I was walking I saw Herman. We had a party. I was glad he was back.

A good **ending** wraps up the narrative.

Herman

Meet the Author

Hanna N.

Grade: one

State: Florida

Hobbies: drawing and reading

What she'd like to be when she grows up: a daycare teacher

Me on the Map

Genre **Nonfiction**

Where in the World?

In the next story, you will read about a girl who finds her place on the map. Watch for all the maps she draws!

Words to Know

could	think
house	world
how	state
over	place
own	find
so	

Practice Sentences

1. The world is a big place.

2. Do you think you could find your place on a map?

3. Here's how I do it.

4. I start with my own house and my street.

5. Then I find my town, my state, and my country.

6. So look over a map and find your place on it.

Meet the Author and the Illustrator

When she was little, **Joan Sweeney** liked art classes. Later she worked at a newspaper. This is her first book.

Annette Cable's pictures show us what our world looks like. She uses maps to show different places. Her drawings make learning about maps fun.

Internet

You can find out more about Joan Sweeney and Annette Cable at Education Place.

www.eduplace.com/kids

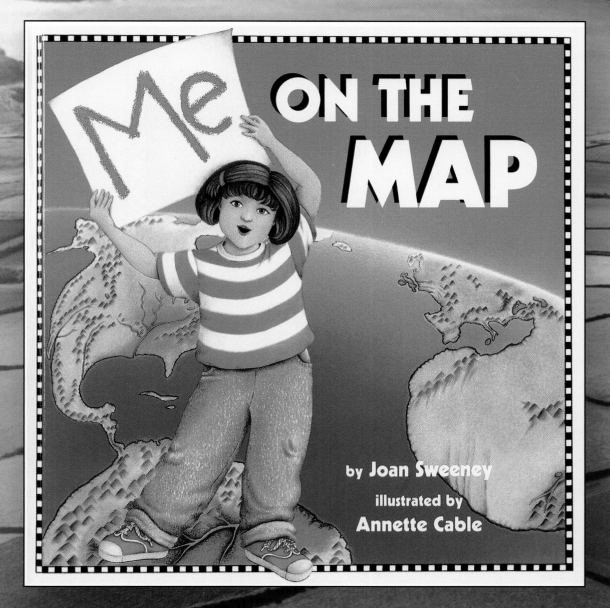

Me ON THE MAP

by **Joan Sweeney**

illustrated by
Annette Cable

Read
Together   Stop partway through the
story and think about some of the
places you have seen.

This is me.
This is me in my room.

This is a map of my room.
This is me on the map of my room.

This is my house.

This is a map of my house.

This is my room on the map of my house.

This is my street.

This is a map of my street.

This is my house on the map of my street.

This is my town.

60

This is a map of my town.
This is my street on the map of my town.

This is my state.

This is a map of my state.
This is my town on the map of my state.

This is my country.
The United States of America.

This is a map of my country.

This is my state on the map of my country.

This is my world. It is called Earth.
It looks like a giant ball.

If you could unroll the world and make it flat . . .

. . . it would look something like this map of the world.

This is my country on the map of the world.

NORTH AMERICA

SOUTH AMERICA

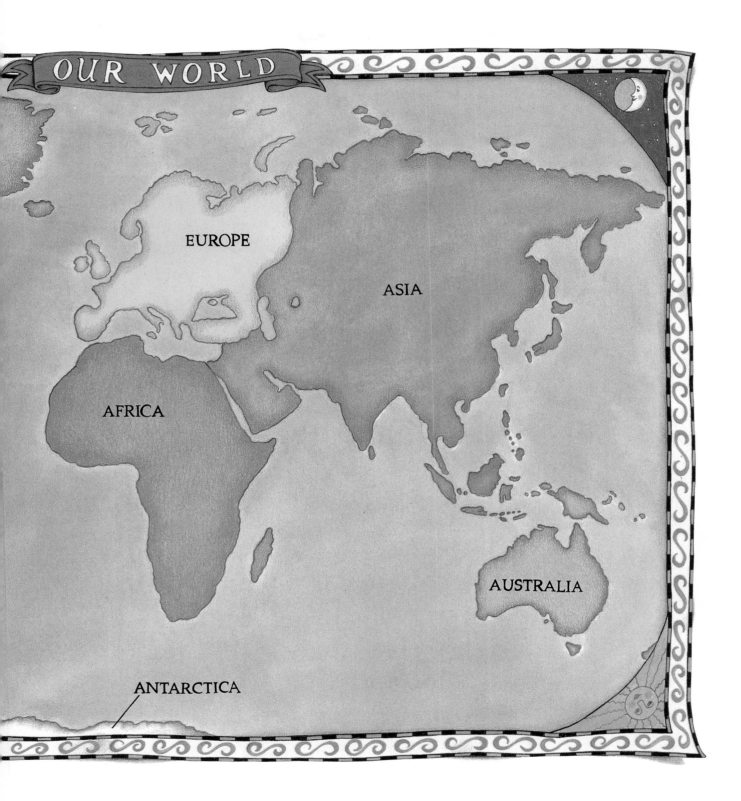

So here's how I find my special place on the map. First I look at the map of the world and find my country.

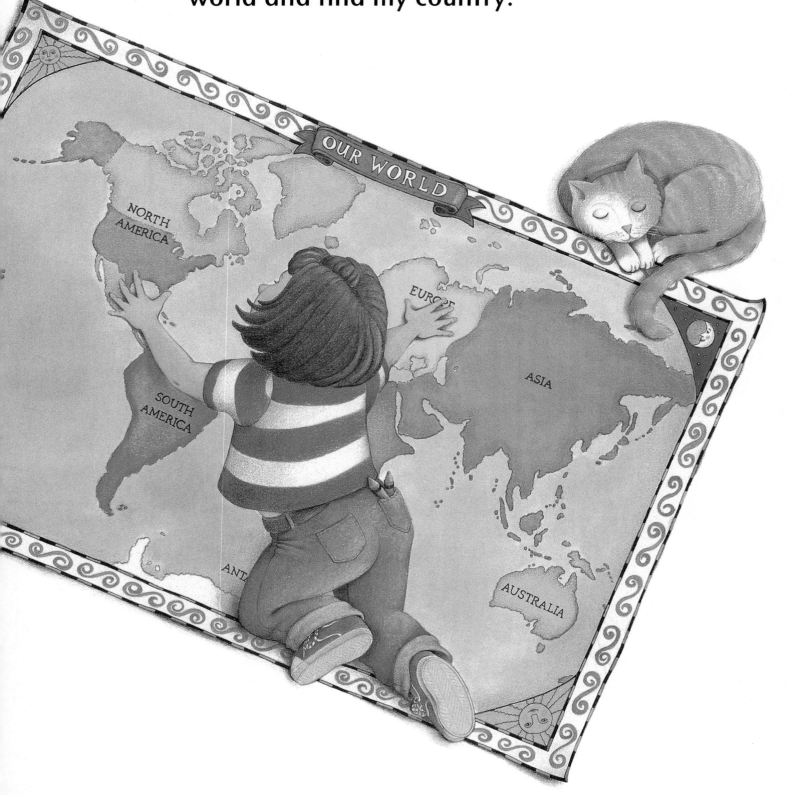

Then I look at the map of my country
and find my state.
Then I look at the map of my state
and find my town.

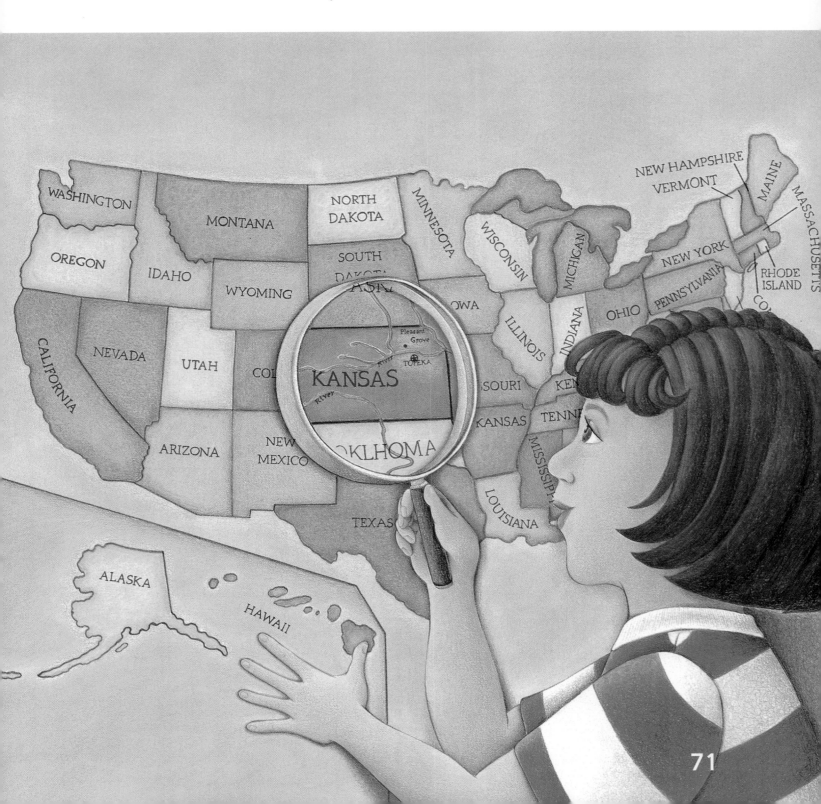

Then I look at the map of my town
and find my street.

And on my street I find my house.

And in my house I find my room.

The map shows: My Brother's Room, My Room, Bath Room, My Mom and Dad's Room, Living Room, Kitchen

And in my room I find me!
Just think . . .

75

. . . in rooms, in houses, on streets, in towns, in countries all over the world, everybody has their own special place on the map.

Just like me.

Just like me on the map.

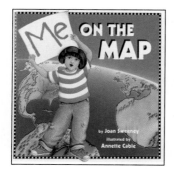

Think About the Story

1. How did the girl learn about her place in the world?

2. How do you think the girl feels about her special place on the map?

3. How would your map be different from the girl's map?

Internet

Complete a Web Word Find

Try finding some of the words from the story in a puzzle. Print out the puzzle from Education Place.

www.eduplace.com/kids

Make a Map

Draw a map of your neighborhood. Include streets, houses, and other buildings you see. Label each place on your map.

 Expressing

Write a Postcard

Write a postcard to a friend. Tell your friend about your special place on the map.

Tips

- **Begin with a greeting.**
- **Write your name at the end.**

Dear Sam,
My special place
is in Los Angeles.

Darren

Los Angeles
California

Read
Together

Children of the World

Maps

Skill: How to Read a Map

- This map shows the world.

- It shows land and water.

- The labels tell the names of the continents, countries, and states.

USA

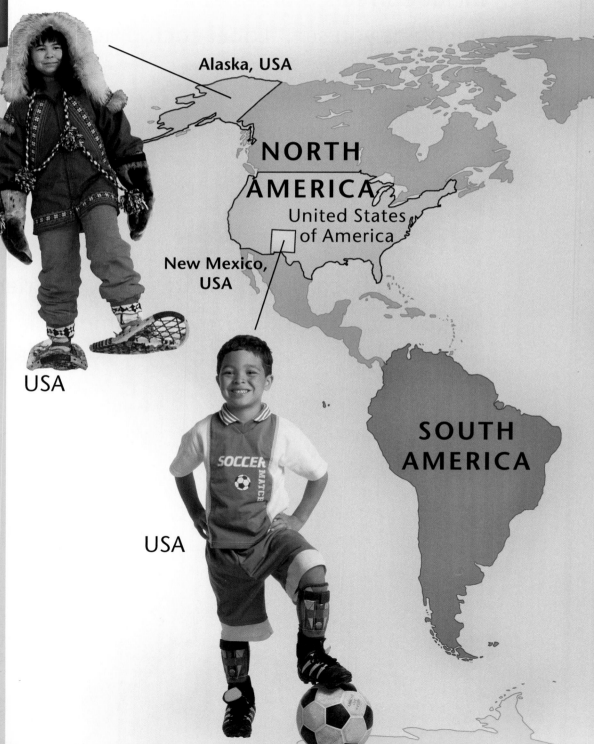

Alaska, USA

NORTH AMERICA

United States of America

New Mexico, USA

USA

SOUTH AMERICA

82

Children all over the world live in many different kinds of homes. Take a look and see where they live!

ASIA

EUROPE

CHINA

China

IVORY COAST

AFRICA

Ivory Coast

AUSTRALIA

ANTARCTICA

This girl lives in Alaska.

Her house is made of wood.

This boy lives in New Mexico.

His house is made of adobe.

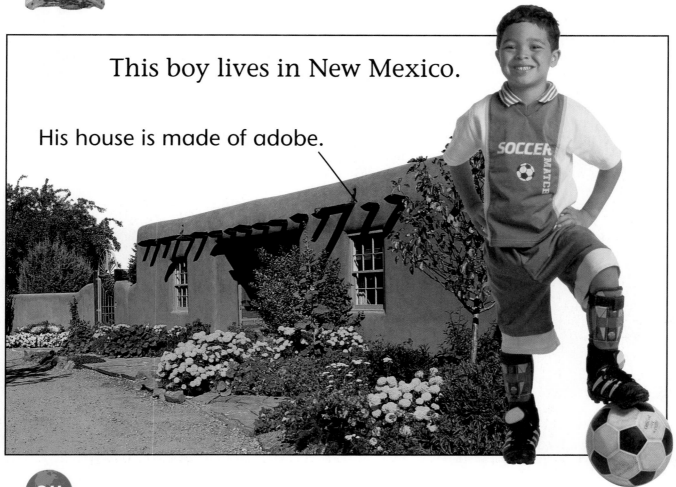

This boy lives in China.

His house has a grass roof.

This girl
lives in the
Ivory Coast.

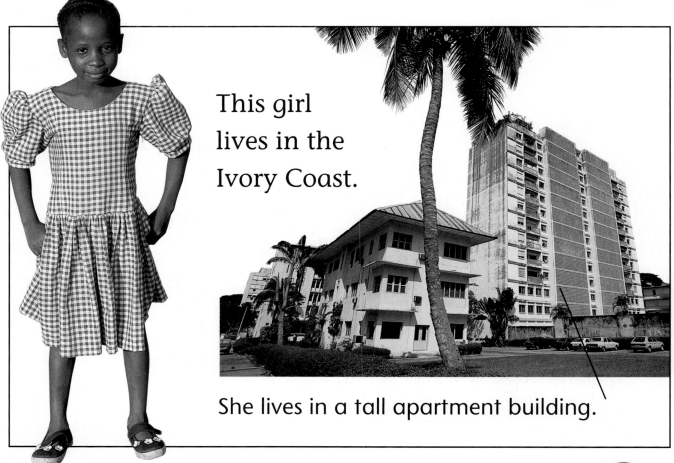

She lives in a tall apartment building.

The Kite

 Genre **Realistic Fiction**

Flying a Kite

Next you will read a story about a mother who makes a kite for her children. When the kite gets lost, the children find a surprise.

Words to Know

give	like
good	she'll
her	can't
little	isn't
try	doesn't
was	didn't
fly	it's
our	we've
kite	

Practice Sentences

1. When Mom was little, she had a kite.
2. She didn't know how to fly it.
3. Her father helped her.
4. We have a kite like Mom's.
5. Isn't that nice?
6. She'll try to get our kite up.
7. If we give it a good push, the kite will fly.
8. It's stuck in a tree and can't come down.
9. We've got to make a new kite.
10. Doesn't it look good?

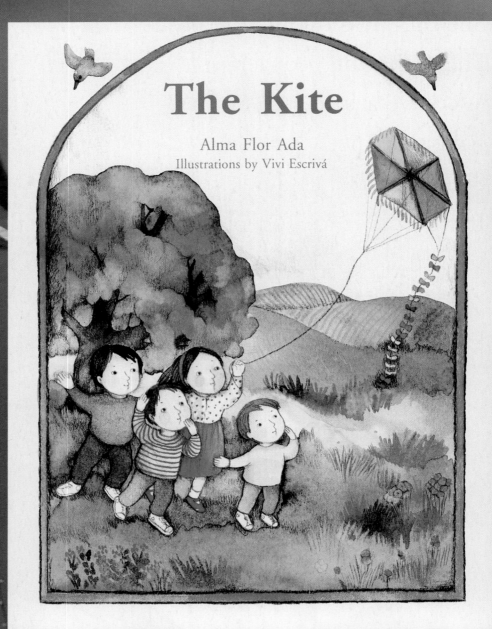

The Kite

Alma Flor Ada

Illustrations by Vivi Escrivá

Strategy Focus

Read Together   Make sure you understand what is happening in the story as you read.

The good news is . . .
Mama says she'll make us a kite like the ones
her father made when she was little.

The bad news is . . .
Mama doesn't know
how to make a kite.

The good news is . . .
Mama can learn.

The bad news is . . .
A kite isn't easy to make.

The good news is . . .
Mama didn't give up.
What a beautiful kite!

The bad news is . . .
It's raining, so we can't fly our kite.

The good news is . . .
The weather is perfect.
At last, we can fly our kite.

The bad news is . . .
The string broke and
the kite got away.

The good news is . . .
Mama says we can try to find it.

The bad news is . . .
We can't find it anywhere.

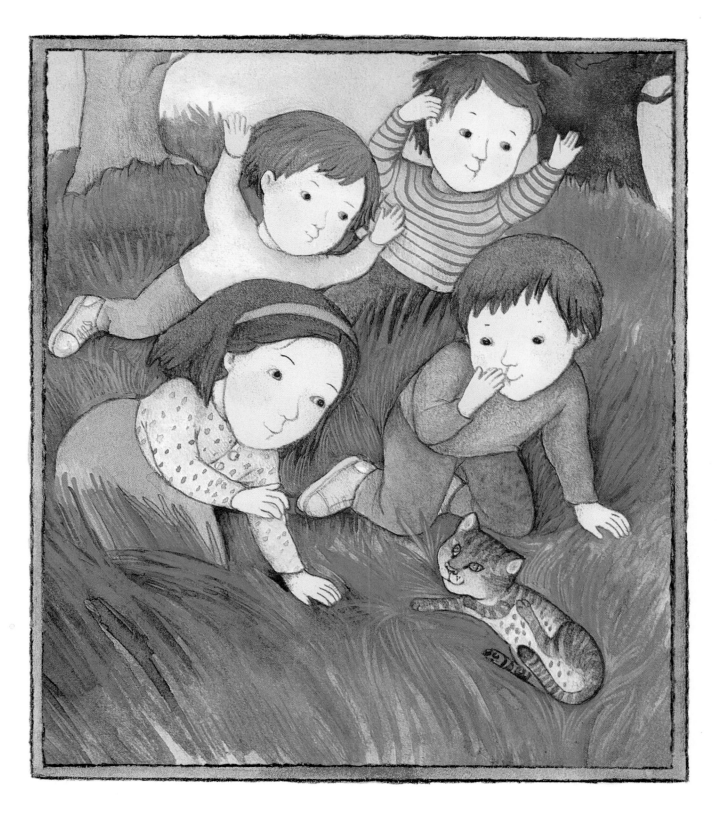

The good news is . . .
We've found a homeless cat.

The bad news is . . .
Mama says we can't take
the cat home with us.

The good news is . . .
We convinced her.

Read Together

Meet the Author

Alma Flor Ada learned to read from her grandmother. When she was nine she knew she would be a writer. Now Alma Flor Ada writes books in Spanish and English. She says that the more you read, the better you will write.

Meet the Illustrator

Vivi Escrivá likes drawing pictures of children having fun. When she was little, she won first prize in an art contest. Later Vivi Escrivá worked for a TV show in Spain.

 Internet

Learn more about Alma Flor Ada and Vivi Escrivá at Education Place.

www.eduplace.com/kids

103

Think About the Story

1. How does the mother learn how to make a kite?

2. What do the children learn from their mother?

3. How would it feel if you lost your kite?

Internet

Take an Online Poll

What is your favorite toy? Visit Education Place and take an online poll.

www.eduplace.com/kids

Weather Picture Dictionary

1. Think about the kinds of weather in the story.

2. Draw and label each kind.

3. Add other kinds of weather you know about.

Explaining

Write Sentences

What do you think happened to the kite in the story? Write some sentences to tell about where the kite might be.

Tips

- **Make a list of some places the kite could be.**
- **Make sure each sentence has a naming word and an action word.**

How to Make a Kite

Genre

Directions

Skill: How to Read Directions

- **Read** the list of materials.

- **Pictures** can give you extra information.

- **Complete** the steps in order.

- **Reread** any part that is unclear.

Materials

- scrap paper

- kite paper (five inches by six inches)

- scissors

- two sticks, five inches and six inches long

- thread

- six feet of ribbon

1 Fold your scrap paper in two. Draw a shape, cut it out, and open it up.

2 Trace your shape onto the kite paper and cut it out. Then make ten holes in your kite.

3 Lace the two sticks in and out of the holes. Cut ten inches of thread and tie it to the six-inch stick.

six-inch stick

4 Make a loop of thread and tie it to the first thread.

5 Tie a new loop to the bottom of the kite. Tie your ribbon to this loop. Your kite is all set to fly!

✔ Phonics

In some tests, your teacher will say a word. You have to find the same sound in another word. Then you fill in the circle to show the correct answer.

1	have	thin	grade	map
	○	○	●	○

Tips

- Put your finger on the number next to the words.

- Find the circle that goes with the correct answer.

- Fill in the whole circle.

Now see how one student figured out the right answer.

My teacher said to listen for the vowel sound. Then she said the word **make**.

I say each word to myself to see which one has the same vowel sound as **make**.

I know that **have, thin**, and **map** do not have the same vowel sound as **make**. **Grade** has the same sound. I will fill in the circle under **grade**.

Poetry

Poetry uses words in interesting ways. Some poems have words that **rhyme**. Some poems are made of parts, or **stanzas**. Some poems **describe** things or tell **stories**. Look and listen to what these poems do.

CONTENTS

Focus on Genre

Turtle, turtle

Turtle, turtle,
I wonder why
Other animals
Pass you by?

Turtles travel
Very slow,
Still I get
Where I want to go.

by Langston Hughes

Quack, Quack!

We have two ducks. One blue. One black.
And when our blue duck goes "Quack-quack"
our black duck quickly quack-quacks back.
The quacks Blue quacks make her quite a quacker
but Black is a quicker quacker-backer.

by Dr. Seuss

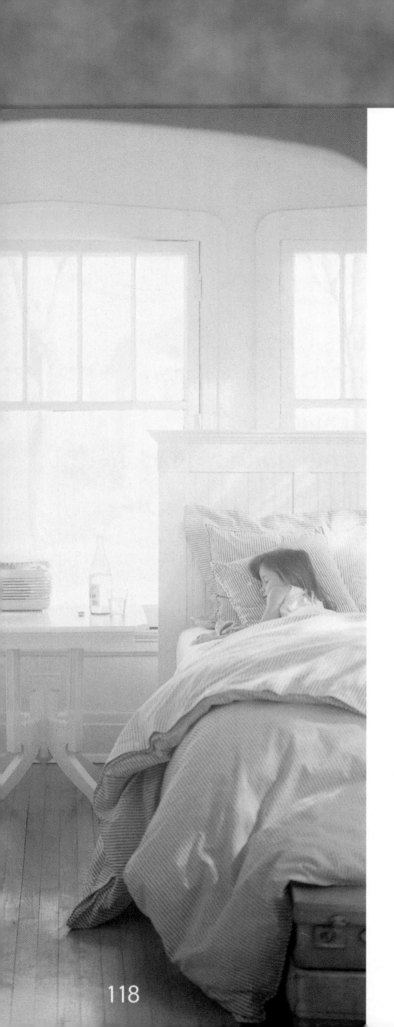

Morning Sun

warming up
my bed
in the morning

the Sun
calls me
through the window

"wake up
get up
come on out"

by Francisco X. Alarcón

Sol matutino

calentando
mi cama
en la mañana

el Sol
me llama
por la ventana

"despierta
levántate
ven afuera"

por Francisco X. Alarcón

The Chipmunk

Chitter-chatter, chitter-chatter
is the chipmunk's steady patter,
even when he's eating acorns
(which he hopes will make him fatter).

by Jack Prelutsky

A little egg
in a nest of hay.
cheep-cheep.
crack-crack.
a little chick
pecked his shell away
cheep-cheep.
crack-crack.

by Tina Anthony
Age 7
England

A discovery!
On my frog's smooth green belly
there sits no button.

Haiku, Yayû

Think About the POETRY

Read Together

1. How is "A discovery" like "Quack, Quack!"? How is it different?

2. Look back at the poem "Morning Sun." How does the poet feel when the sun wakes him up?

3. Which animal poem do you think describes the animal best? What words describe the animal?

4. Which poem is your favorite? Why?

Internet

Send an E-Postcard

Send an e-postcard to a friend. Tell about your favorite poem. You can find a postcard at Education Place.

www.eduplace.com/kids

Creating

Write a Poem

You can write your own poem. Here's how to do it:

1. Choose a subject that you want to write about.
2. Decide if your poem will have rhyming words.
3. Think of some interesting ways to describe your subject.

When you finish, share your poem with others. Make a class poetry book by putting all your poems together.

127

Animal Adventures

Two Feet, Four Feet

I have only two small feet,
But horses, dogs, and cows
   Have four.
I can walk and run with
   Mine.
So why do **they** need any
   More?

by Ilo Orleans

129

The Sleeping Pig
written by Carmen Tafolla and Jan Epton Seale
illustrated by Rosario Valderrama

The Sleeping Pig

Genre Fantasy

How to Wake a Pig

In the next story, you'll read about a pig who won't get out of a watermelon patch. A small hero finally gets the pig to move.

Words to Know

morning	woke
found	nose
shout	whole
by	huge
out	use
show	tune
climb	went
go	lift
home	

Practice Sentences

1. If you went by your bed one morning and found a huge pig, would you lift it out?
2. You could walk by and shout, "Go home!"
3. Then climb up and tap the pig's small nose.
4. Sing a tune.
5. You could use the whole day to wake the pig.
6. Once you woke the pig, you could show it how to get home.

Good Morning

Meet the Authors

Carmen Tafolla

Jan Epton Seale

The authors first wrote this story in Spanish. Carmen Tafolla and Jan Epton Seale both live in Texas. Jan Epton Seale lives near Mexico. Carmen Tafolla has a daughter named Mari.

Internet

You can learn more about Carmen Tafolla and Jan Epton Seale at Education Place.

www.eduplace.com/kids

The Sleeping Pig

written by Carmen Tafolla and Jan Epton Seale
illustrated by Rosario Valderrama

Strategy Focus

Read Together As you read, stop and think about what each animal does to wake Mrs. Pig.

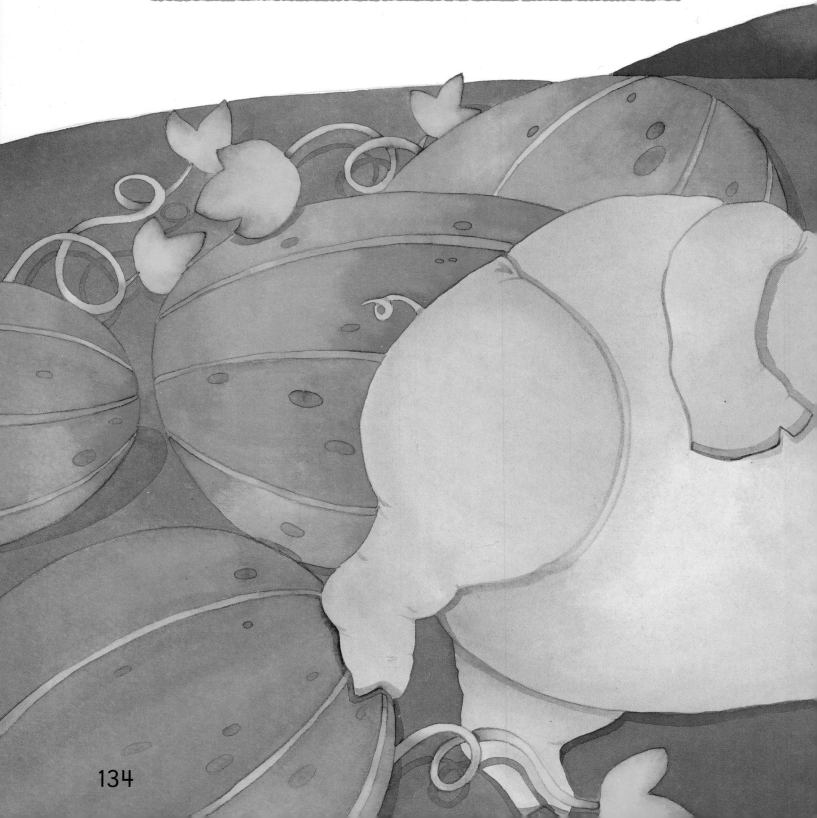

One morning, Celina found a huge pig sleeping in the watermelon patch.

Celina began to shout. "Go home, Mrs. Pig! I wish you would go. You can't rest here in the watermelon patch. I can't pick my watermelons."

But huge Mrs. Pig didn't wake up.

A coyote came by and said, "Let me show
you how to get Mrs. Pig out of the patch."
The coyote began to howl and howl.

But huge Mrs. Pig did not wake up.

139

A mule came by and said, "I can make Mrs. Pig climb out of the patch." The mule began to push and push.

But huge Mrs. Pig went on sleeping.

A rabbit came by and said, "I will get Mrs. Pig out of the patch for you." The rabbit began to hop and hop.

But huge Mrs. Pig went on sleeping.

A snake came by and said, "I will use my tail to lift Mrs. Pig out of the patch." The snake began to pull and pull.

But huge Mrs. Pig wouldn't wake up.

144

Then a cricket came by and said, "I know I am small and Mrs. Pig is huge. But just look at what I can do."

The cricket began to sing a tune.
Chirrr-chirrr-chirrr! Di-di-di-di!

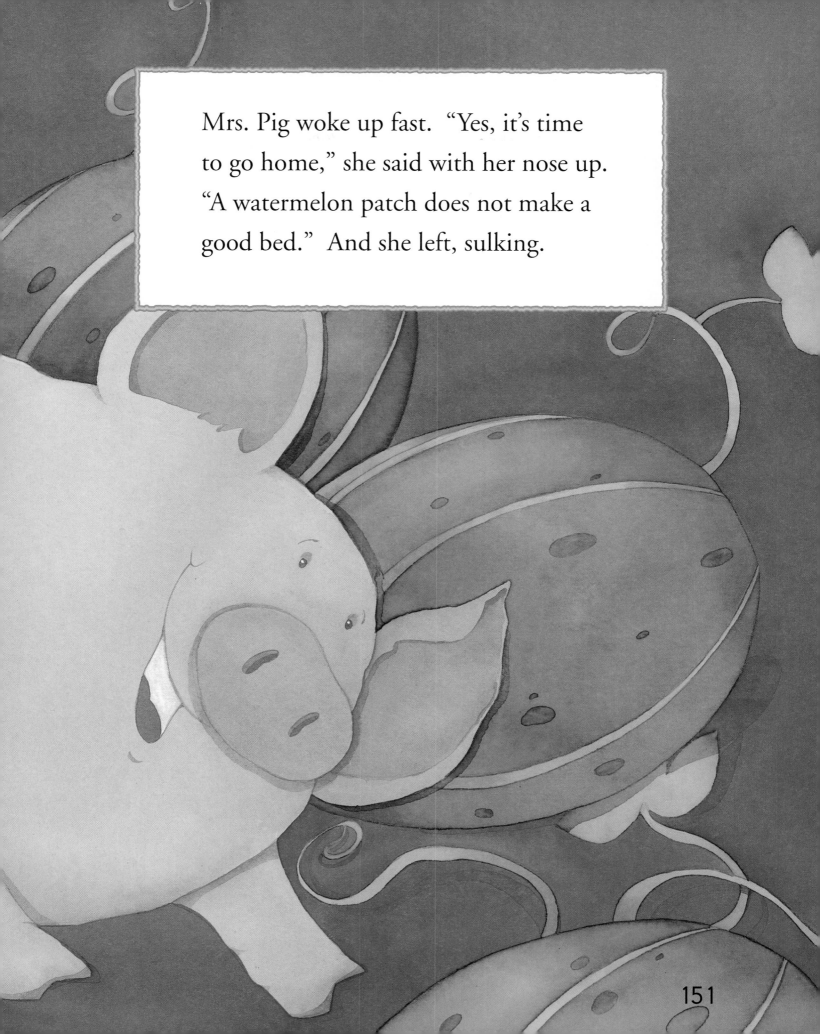

Mrs. Pig woke up fast. "Yes, it's time to go home," she said with her nose up. "A watermelon patch does not make a good bed." And she left, sulking.

Celina thanked the small cricket. Then they ate a whole watermelon to celebrate!

Read Together

Meet the Illustrator
Rosario Valderrama

Rosario Valderrama was born in
Mexico City. When she draws, she tries
to remember the things she loved as a
child. She says young artists should try
to show their worlds to others.

Internet

To find out more about Rosario Valderrama, visit
Education Place. **www.eduplace.com/kids**

Think About the Story

Read Together

The Sleeping Pig
written by Carmen Tafolla and Jan Epton Seale
illustrated by Rosario Valderrama

1. How did Celina feel when she saw Mrs. Pig?

2. Why was the cricket the only animal who could wake Mrs. Pig?

3. What would you do if you were Celina?

Internet

Print Out Puppets

Print out story character puppets from Education Place to retell the story.

www.eduplace.com/kids

Make an Award

Make an award for the hero in the story. Write a title for your award.

Explaining

Write a Poster

How would you wake a sleeping pig? Draw a poster and write one sentence. Share your poster with the class.

Tips

- **Think about some ways to wake up a pig.**
- **Make sure that your drawing and your sentence match.**

Social
Studies
Link

Read
Together

Genre

Social Studies
Article

Skill: How to
Read a Social
Studies Article

- **Look** at the title and pictures.

- **Think** about what you know.

- **Predict** what you will learn.

- **Reread** if you do not understand.

What Is a Desert?

A desert is a dry place that gets little or no rain. There are many deserts all over the world.

Cactus plants can grow in a desert. They can hold water for a long time. Some cactuses are as big as trees.

Arizona, USA

Namibia, Africa

Flowering Agave

Saguaro cactus

Claret Cup cactus

Birds, mice, snakes, and lizards are some of the animals that live in the desert.

Ostrich

The scorpion also makes its home in the desert.

Flap-Necked Chameleon

Rattlesnake

Scorpion

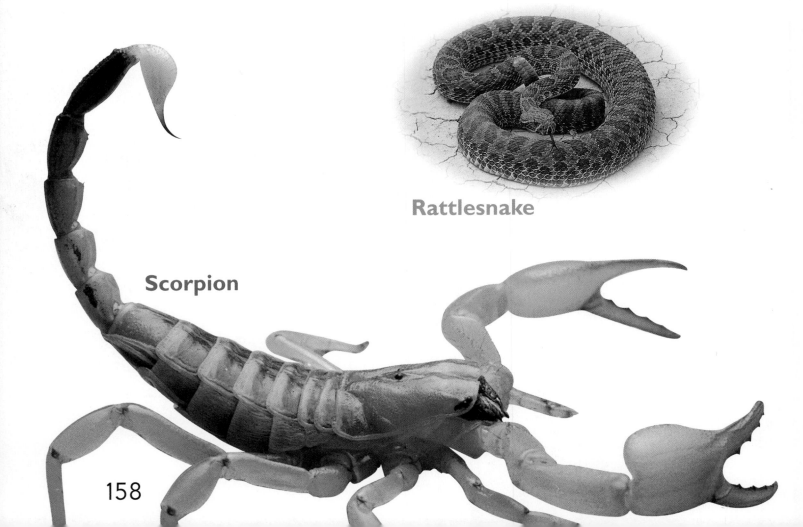

Some people move through the desert on camels. Camels can go days without food or water.

Would you like to see a desert?

A Description

A description is a picture in words that helps the reader to see, hear, taste, feel, and smell what you're writing about. Use this student writing as a model when you write your own description.

> A good **beginning** tells what the description is about.

> A good description includes **sense** words.

Fishing with My Dad

I have a big fishing rod with a small hook at the end. When I go fishing with my Dad, this is what I use. My Dad's fishing rod is tall and yellow with a big hook at the end.

160

He usually catches huge gray catfish.
I usually catch small minnows.

A good description uses **details**.

Meet the Author

Megan S.
Grade: one
State: Delaware
Hobbies: fishing, reading, and writing
What she'd like to be when she grows up: a teacher

EEK! There's a Mouse in the House

Genre Fantasy

Animals in the House

In the next story, you'll read about some animals that mess up a little girl's house! How can she get rid of them?

Words to Know

cow	wall
table	me
now	he
door	EEK
there	sheep
through	eating
horse	

Practice Sentences

1. A cow, a sheep, and a horse came
   to a house.
2. "Now what could be in there?"
   asked the horse.
3. He went through the door.
4. The others went through, too.
5. By the wall was a table of things
   to eat.
6. A mouse was eating on the table.
7. "EEK!" said the cow and the sheep.
8. "The mouse can't hurt me," said
   the horse.

163

EEK!
There's a Mouse in the House

WONG HERBERT YEE

⭐ **Strategy Focus**

🔲 Read Together As you read the story, ask yourself about each animal and what it does.

EEK!

There's a mouse in the house.

Send in the cat
to chase that rat!

Uh-oh!

The cat knocked over a lamp.

Send in the dog
to catch that scamp!

Dear me!

The dog has broken a dish.

And now the cat is after the fish.

Send in the hog
to shoo that dog!

Oh my!

The hog is eating the cake.

Sending the hog
was a big mistake.

Send in the cow.

Send that cow NOW!

Oh no!

The cow is dancing with a mop.

Send in the sheep to make her stop!

Goodness!

The sheep is tangled
in yarn.

Send in the hen
from the barn!

Mercy!

The hen is laying eggs
on the table.

Send in the horse
from the stable!

Heavens!

The horse kicked a hole
in the wall.

Send in the elephant
to get rid of them ALL!

The elephant was BIG,
but he squeezed through the door.

Once he was in,
there was room for no more.

Out of the house marched
the cat and the cow.

Out came the horse and
the hen and the hog.

Out walked the sheep.

Out ran the dog.

But then from within,
there came a shout:

EEK! There's a mouse in the house!

Meet the Author and Illustrator

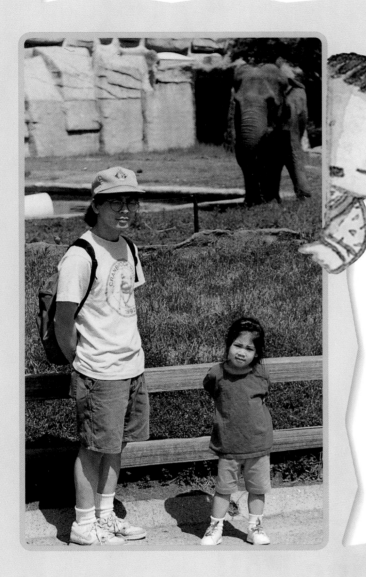

This is **Wong Herbert Yee**'s first children's book. While he was writing it, he read it to his young daughter, Ellen. If she laughed at a sentence, he kept it in the story.

 Internet

Find out more about Wong Herbert Yee at Education Place.

www.eduplace.com/kids

EEK!
There's a Mouse in the House

WONG HERBERT YEE

Think About the Story

1. How did the girl feel about the mouse?

2. Was it a good idea for the girl to call in the animals? Why?

3. What would you do if you were the girl in this story?

Internet

Take an Online Poll

What animal from *EEK! There's a Mouse in the House* would you want for a pet? Visit Education Place to place your vote.

www.eduplace.com/kids

Act Out the Story

Act out the story with some partners. Each of you can be a different character. Make sure to use each character's actions.

Write a List

Pick an animal from the story. Make a list of clean-up chores for the animal.

Tips

- **Think about what the animal needs to clean up.**
- **Number each thing on your list.**

Cat

1. Pick up the lamp.

Pictographs

Skill: How to Read a Pictograph

- A pictograph is a chart that uses pictures to compare things.

- These pictographs show the size of animals compared to people.

Animals Big and Small

Animals come in many shapes and sizes. Let's look at some of the biggest and smallest animals in the world.

Blue Whale

The biggest animal in the world is the blue whale. It can grow to 100 feet long. That's longer than sixteen six-foot men lying head to toe!

Giraffe

- Giraffes are the tallest animals in the world.
- Some giraffes grow as tall as nineteen feet.
- That's taller than three men standing on top of each other's shoulders!

Harvest Mouse

Some harvest mice are no more than three inches long. That's about as long as a grown-up's finger!

Bee Hummingbird

The bee hummingbird from Cuba is just two inches long. That's shorter than a grown-up's thumb!

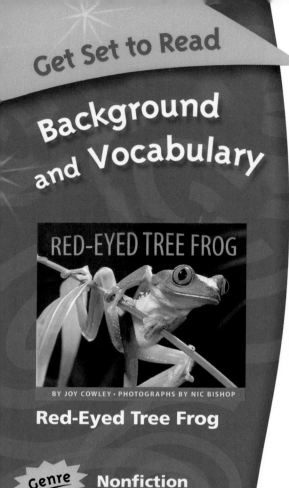

Red-Eyed Tree Frog

RED-EYED TREE FROG

BY JOY COWLEY · PHOTOGRAPHS BY NIC BISHOP

Genre   Nonfiction

A Visit to the Rain Forest

You will read about a day in the life of a red-eyed tree frog in the next story.

Words to Know

been	evening
far	near
forest	rain
goes	wait
hungry	day
soon	away

Practice Sentences

1. My mom has been to the rain forest.

2. It's far away from where we live.

3. I will go the next time Mom goes.

4. We will hike all day.

5. When we are hungry, we will stop and eat.

6. We will spend the evening in a tent.

7. We will sit near a tree and wait for a red-eyed tree frog.

8. I hope we go soon!

RED-EYED TREE FROG

BY JOY COWLEY · PHOTOGRAPHS BY NIC BISHOP

Strategy Focus

Read Together What do you think the red-eyed tree frog will do? Read the story to find out.

192

Evening comes to the rain forest.

The macaw
and the toucan
will soon go to sleep.

194

But the red-eyed tree frog has
been asleep all day.

It wakes up hungry.
What will it eat?

Here is an iguana.
Frogs do not eat iguanas.

Do iguanas eat frogs?
The red-eyed tree frog does
not wait to find out.
It hops onto another branch.

The frog is hungry but it will
not eat the ant.

It will not eat the katydid.

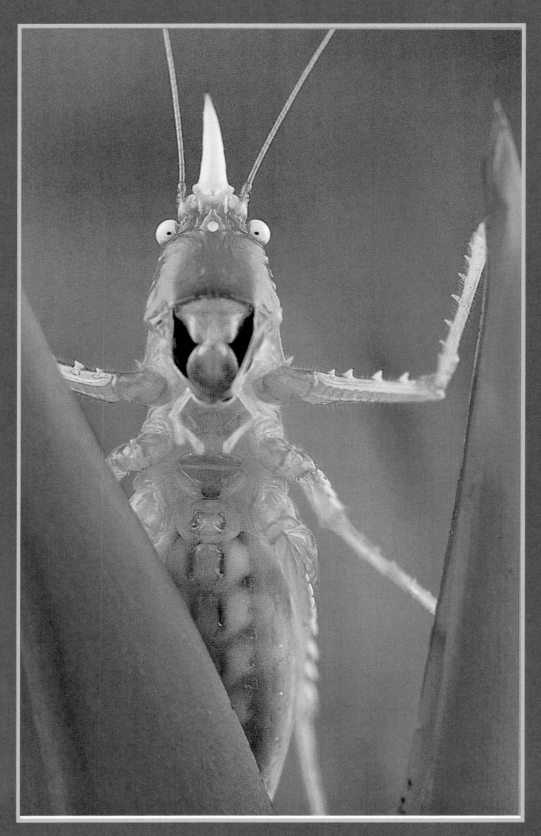

Will it eat the caterpillar?
No!

The caterpillar is poisonous.

Something moves near the frog.
Something slips and slithers along a branch.
It is a hungry boa snake.

The snake flicks its tongue.
It tastes frog in the air.
Look out, frog!

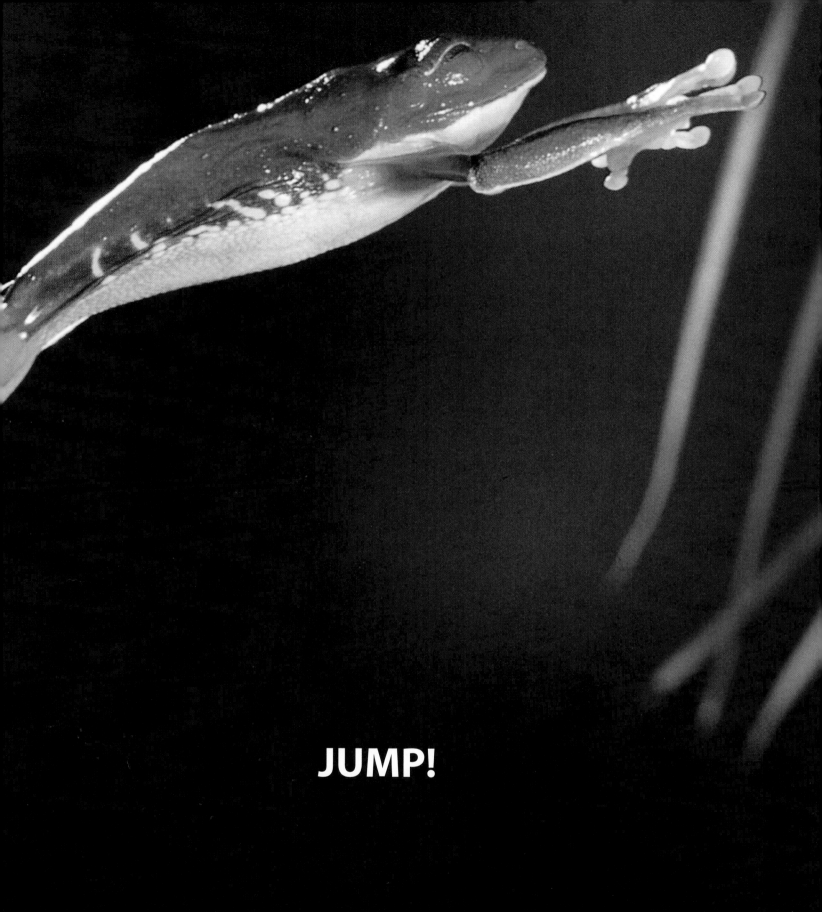

JUMP!

JUMP!

The frog lands on a leaf,
far away from the boa.
What does the frog see on
the leaf?

A moth!

Crunch, crunch, crunch!

The tree frog is no longer hungry.
It climbs onto a leaf.

The red-eyed tree frog shuts its eyes . . .

and goes to sleep . . .

as morning comes to the rain forest.

Meet the Author and the Photographer

Joy Cowley loves animals, especially frogs. When she saw these pictures, she liked them very much. She decided to write a children's book to go with them.

Nic Bishop went to the rain forest to take photographs of the red-eyed tree frogs. One frog became a family pet.

Internet

Visit Education Place to learn more about Joy Cowley and Nic Bishop.

www.eduplace.com/kids

RED-EYED TREE FROG

BY JOY COWLEY · PHOTOGRAPHS BY NIC BISHOP

Think About the Story

1. Do you think this rain forest is quiet or noisy? Why?

2. What do you think the red-eyed tree frog has learned about living in the rain forest?

3. Would you like to visit the rain forest? Why?

Internet

Go on a Web Field Trip

Visit a rain forest at Education Place.

www.eduplace.com/kids

Comparing Sizes

A red-eyed tree frog is nearly as long as this ruler. Find things in your classroom that are about the same size.

Creating

Write a Riddle

Write a riddle about one of the animals in the story. Have a partner read your riddle and guess the animal.

Tips

- **Study a picture of the animal.**
- **Use describing words.**

Who has a yellow stripe and many legs?

Genre

Poetry

Skill: How to Read a Poem

- **Read** the title to see what the poem is about.

- **Read** the poem.

- **Listen** for any rhyming words.

The Snake

Don't ever make
the bad mistake
of stepping on
the sleeping snake

because
his jaws

might be awake.

by Jack Prelutsky

Snake, 20th century,
Niki de Saint-Phalle, b. 1930, French
painted polyester

THE TOUCAN

Of all the birds I know, few can
Boast of as large a bill as the toucan.
Yet I can think of one who can,
And if you think a while, too, you can:
Another toucan
In the zoo can.

by Pyke Johnson, Jr.

Toucan Design on Mola, San Blas Archipelago, Panama

Filling in the Blank

Some tests have sentences with a blank in them. You must decide which answer choice best fills in the blank. Look at this sample test for *Red-Eyed Tree Frog*. The correct answer is shown.

Read the sentence. Fill in the circle next to the best answer.

1   The red-eyed tree frog _____ all day.

   ● sleeps   ○ climbs   ○ eats

Tips

- Put your finger on the number next to the sentence.

- Find the circle that goes with the correct answer.

- Fill in the whole circle.

Now see how one student figured out the best answer.

First, I read the directions. Then I read the test sentence. I need to find out what the frog does all day.

I look back in the story. The beginning tells what the frog does. I will look there.

I read the test sentence to myself, using each answer choice. The last two choices do not tell about the frog in the daytime. The first choice is best.

A

anywhere
Anywhere means in any place. You can sit
anywhere you like.

B

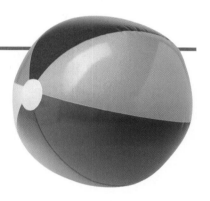

ball
A **ball** is something that is round.
Miguel hit the **ball** with the bat.

barn
A **barn** is a kind of building on a farm. A
farmer keeps his cows and pigs in the **barn**.

beautiful
Beautiful means very nice to look at or hear.
Anna drew a picture of a **beautiful** rainbow.

began
To **begin** means to start. School **began**
in September.

boa

A **boa** is a kind of snake. A **boa** can live in the rain forest.

C

caterpillar

A **caterpillar** is an insect that looks like a worm. A **caterpillar** will change into a butterfly.

celebrate

To **celebrate** is to do something special for an event. We went to the park to **celebrate** my birthday.

convinced

To **convince** means to talk someone into something. I **convinced** my mother to let me go on the trip.

country

A **country** is a place where people live and share the same laws. There are many **countries** in the world.

coyote

A **coyote** is an animal that looks like a small wolf. The **coyote** didn't look much bigger than a dog.

cricket

A **cricket** is a small insect that looks like a grasshopper. Jamal saw the **cricket** jump.

D

dancing

To **dance** means to move your body to music. Jan and her friends like **dancing** at parties.

E

Earth

Earth is the planet we live on. **Earth** looks round when you see it from space.

easy

Easy means not hard to do. Riding my bike is **easy**.

elephant

An **elephant** is a very big animal with thick skin, big ears, and a long trunk. The **elephant** was the biggest animal in the circus.

eyes

Eyes are the parts of the body that let it see. The kitten closed its **eyes** and went to sleep.

F

fancy

Fancy means prettier or better than usual. We had a **fancy** cake at the party.

G

giant

Giant means much bigger than usual. Michael looked up at the **giant** tree.

H

heavy

Heavy means hard to lift. The box of toys was too **heavy** to carry.

hide

To **hide** something is to put it where nobody will see it. When I **hide**, my friends can't find me.

howl

To **howl** is to make a long cry like a dog, coyote, or wolf. My dog will **howl** when she's lonely.

I

iguana

An **iguana** is a kind of lizard. Tanya wanted an **iguana** for a pet.

inside

To be **inside** means to be in something. I'm staying **inside** the house because it's raining.

K

katydid

A **katydid** is a large green insect like a grasshopper. A **katydid** will rub its wings together to make a noise.

L

laying

To **lay** an egg is to make an egg. The hen was **laying** eggs in her nest.

M

macaw

A **macaw** is a large parrot.
The **macaw** has a strong, curved beak.

marched

To **march** with someone is to take the same size steps at the same time. The band **marched** in the big parade.

mercy

To say **Mercy** is to show surprise. **Mercy**! That was a close call.

mouse

A **mouse** is a very small animal with a
long tail, short fur, and sharp teeth.
The **mouse** likes to eat cheese.

moves

To **move** is to go from one place to another.
A bird **moves** from tree to tree by flying.

N

news

News is a story about things that are
happening. My mother watches the **news**
on television.

P

perfect

If something is **perfect**, it is just right.
It was a **perfect** day for flying our kite.

plain

Plain means very simple. I put my lunch
in a **plain** brown paper bag.

poisonous

A **poison** is something that can cause sickness or death. A rattlesnake is a **poisonous** animal.

R

rabbit

A **rabbit** is an animal with long ears and soft fur. A **rabbit** can hop very fast.

raining

To **rain** means to fall as drops of water. Get your umbrella because it's **raining**.

rough

Something that is **rough** does not feel even. The bumpy road was very **rough**.

S

smooth

Something that is **smooth** feels even and has no rough spots. The ice at the rink was very **smooth**.

special

Special means important and not like all the rest. Holidays and birthdays are **special** days.

street

A **street** is a road in a city or town. Sue lives on a busy **street**.

T

tail

A **tail** is part of an animal's body. Laura's dog wags its **tail** when it gets a treat.

tangled

Tangle means to be all mixed up. The kite's string got **tangled** in the tree.

tongue

The **tongue** is a part of the body inside the mouth. Your **tongue** helps you eat and speak.

toucan

A **toucan** is a colorful bird with a very long, large bill. Amy was excited to see a **toucan** flying in the rain forest.

town

A **town** is a place where people live and work. My **town** is smaller than a city.

W

wait

To **wait** means to stay someplace until something happens. We **wait** at the corner until the school bus comes.

watermelon

A **watermelon** is a big sweet fruit that is pink or red inside. **Watermelon** is a good snack in the summer.

weather

Weather is what it is like outside. Jim goes swimming in warm **weather**.

Acknowledgments

For each of the selections listed below, grateful acknowledgment is made for permission to excerpt and/or reprint original or copyrighted material, as follows:

Selections

EEK! There's a Mouse in the House, by Wong Herbert Yee. Copyright © 1992 by Wong Herbert Yee. Reprinted by permission of Houghton Mifflin Company. All rights reserved.

The Kite, by Alma Flor Ada, illustrated by Vivi Escrivá. Copyright © 1999 by Santillana USA Publishing Co., Inc. Reprinted by permission of the publisher.

Me on the Map, by Joan Sweeney, illustrated by Annette Cable. Text copyright © 1996 by Joan Sweeney. Illustrations copyright © 1996 by Annette Cable. Published by arrangement with Random House Children's Books, a division of Random House, Inc., New York, New York, U.S.A. All rights reserved.

Moving Day, by Robert Kalan, illustrated by Yossi Abolafia. Text copyright © 1996 by Robert Kalan. Illustrations copyright © 1996 by Yossi Abolafia. Reprinted by permission of HarperCollins Publishers.

Red-Eyed Tree Frog, by Joy Cowley, photographs by Nic Bishop, published by Scholastic Press, a division of Scholastic Inc. Text copyright © 1999 by Joy Cowley, Photographs copyright © 1999 by Nic Bishop. Reprinted by permission of Scholastic Inc.

Poetry

"A discovery!" by Yayû, translated by Sylvia Cassedy and Kunihiro Suetake, from *Birds, Frogs and Moonlight.* Copyright © 1967 by Doubleday and Co. Reprinted by permission of Ellen Cassedy.

"A little egg," by Tina Anthony from *Miracles: Poems by Children of the English Speaking World,* edited by Richard Lewis. Copyright © 1966 by Richard Lewis. Used with permission of Richard Lewis.

"The Chipmunk" from *Zoo Doings,* by Jack Prelutsky. Copyright © 1983 by Jack Prelutsky. Reprinted by permission of HarperCollins Publishers.

"Morning Sun/Sol matutino" from *Laughing Tomatoes and Other Spring Poems/Jitomates risueños y otros poemas de primavera,* by Francisco X. Alarcón. Copyright © 1997 by Francisco Alarcón. Reprinted by permission of the publisher, Children's Book Press, San Francisco, CA.

"Quack, Quack!" from *Oh Say Can You Say?,* by Dr. Seuss, TM & Copyright © by Dr. Seuss Enterprises, L.P., 1979. Reprinted by permission of Random House Children's Books, a division of Random House, Inc.

"The Snake" from *Zoo Doings,* by Jack Prelutsky. Copyright © 1983 by Jack Prelutsky. Reprinted by permission of HarperCollins Publishers.

"The Toucan" from *Pyke's Poems,* by Pyke Johnson, Jr., published by Shorelands Publishing Company. Copyright © by Pyke Johnson, Jr. Reprinted by permission of the author.

"Turtle, turtle" from *The Sweet and Sour Animal Book,* by Langston Hughes. Copyright © 1994 (text) by Romana Bass & Arnold Rampersad, Administrators of the Estate of Langston Hughes. Used by permission of Oxford University Press, Inc., and Harold Ober Associates, Inc.

"Two Feet, Four Feet," by Ilo Orleans. Copyright © 1992 by Ilo Orleans. Reprinted by permission of Karen S. Solomon.

Illustration from *Waiting for Wings,* by Lois Ehlert, is depicted on the Focus on Poetry Table of Contents page. Copyright © 2001 by Lois Ehlert. Reprinted by permission of Harcourt, Inc.

Special thanks to the following teachers whose students' compositions appear as Student Writing Models: Cheryl Claxton, Florida; Patricia Kopay, Delaware; Susana Llanes, Michigan; Joan Rubens, Delaware; Nancy Schulten, Kentucky; Linda Wallis, California

Credits

Photography

3 (t) Navaswan/Taxi/Getty Images. (b) Siede Preis/PhotoDisc Green/Getty Images. **5,6** © Navaswan/Taxi/Getty Images. **7** (l) © PhotoDisc/Getty Images. (r) Tim Davis/Photo Researchers, Inc. **9,11** © Siede Preis/PhotoDisc Green/Getty Images. **12-13** (bkgd) From *Look-Alikes, Jr.* by Joan Steiner. Copyright © 1999 by Joan Steiner. Photography by Thomas Lindley. **13** (m) © Navaswan/Taxi/Getty Images. **16** (bkgd) © Georgette Douwma/Taxi/Getty Images. **43** (t) Courtesy William Morrow. **44** (l) © PhotoDisc/Getty Images. (r) Artville. **46** (t) CORBIS/Stuart Westmorland. (b) J.H. (Pete) Carmichael. **47** (t) Dave King/Dorling Kindersley. (b) J.H. (Pete) Carmichael. **48** NHPA/Anthony Bannister. **49** CORBIS/Annie Griffiths Belt. **54** (t) John Zich/Mercury Pictures. (b) Courtesy Annette Cable. **54-5** (bkgd) © Charles O'Rear/Corbis. **82** (t) Chris Arend/Alaska Stock Images. (b) Rubberball Productions. **83** (t) Jian Chen/Stock Connection/PictureQuest. (b) Michael Dwyer/Stock Boston/PictureQuest. **84** (tl) Chris Arend/Alaska Stock Images. (tr) CORBIS/Galen Rowell. (bl) Garry Adams/ IndexStock. (br) Rubberball Productions. **85** (tl) CORBIS/The Purcell Team. (tr) Jian Chen/Stock Connection/PictureQuest. (bl) Michael Dwyer/Stock Boston/PictureQuest. (br) Christopher Morris/Black Star/PictureQuest. **88-9** (bkgd) © Zephyr Picture/ Index Stock Imagery/PictureQuest. **102** Courtesy Alma Flor Ada. **103** Courtesy Vivi Escrivá. **106–9** (bkgd) © PhotoDisc/Getty Images. **108** Lynda Richardson. **109** (t) Lawrence Migdale/Stock Boston. (b) Lynda Richardson. **114–5** © PhotoDisc/Getty Images. **116** Tim Davis/Stone/Getty Images. **117** Paul Chauncey/CORBIS. **118** Laurie Rubin/The Image Bank/Getty Images. **120** Daniel J. Cox/Stone/Getty Images. **122–3** Tim Davis/Photo Researchers, Inc. **124–5** Frank Moscati/CORBIS. **126** John Lei/Stock Boston. **128-9** (bkgd) © Ariel Skelley/CORBIS. **129** (m) © Siede Preis/PhotoDisc Green/Getty Images. **132** (l) Courtesy Carmen Tafolla. (r) Paul Buck/Mercury Pictures. **132-3** (bkgd) Kathryn Kleinman/FoodPix/Getty Images. **153** Courtesy Rosario Valeramma. **156–7** © Jim Brandenburg/Minden Pictures. **156** (bl) © Carr Clifton/Minden Pictures. (br) © Jim Brandenburg/Minden Pictures. **157** (bl) Frans Lanting/Minden Pictures. (bm) Brian Stablyk/Stone/Getty Images. (br) Kerrick James/Stone/Getty Images. **158** (t) (m) (bl) Frans Lanting/Minden Pictures. (br) © Jim Brandenburg/Minden Pictures. **159** Will & Deni McIntyre/Stone/ Getty Images. **160** © PhotoDisc/Getty Images. **164-5** (bkgd) © Albert Normandin/Masterfile. **183** Courtesy Wong Herbert Yee. **186–7** Mike Johnson Marine Natural History Photography. **188** Corbis Royalty Free. **189** (t) CORBIS/ George McCarthy. (b) Robert Tyrrell Photography. **190** © Nic Bishop Photography. **192** (bkgd) © R. Watts/Premium/ Panoramic Images. **215** (tl) © Terry Coles. (tr) Michael P.L. Fogden/ Bruce Coleman/PictureQuest. (bl) David Aubrey/CORBIS. (br) Courtesy Nic Bishop. **216** © PhotoDisc/Getty Images. **217** CORBIS/David A. Northcott. **218** Snake, 20th century. Niki de Saint-Phalle, b. 1930, French. painted polyester. 59 in height. Private Collection. Christie's Images, Inc. **219** CORBIS/Kevin Schafer. **222** © PhotoDisc/Getty Images. **223** Kim Taylor/Dorling Kindersley. **224** © PhotoDisc/Getty Images. **225** © PhotoDisc/Getty Images. **226** PhotoSpin. **227** (t) Artville. (b) © PhotoDisc/Getty Images. **228** © PhotoDisc/Getty Images. **229** © PhotoDisc/Getty Images. **231** (t) ©Frans Lanting/Minden Pictures. (b) Artville.

Assignment Photography

15, 45 (t), **53, 80. 105** © HMCo./Joel Benjamin. **111, 221** © HMCo./Michael Indresano Photography. **131, 163, 184** © HMCo./Michelle Joyce. **155, 185** © HMCo./Allan Landau.

Illustration

87 Toby Williams. **112-113** Lois Ehlert. **115–126** (borders) Eileen Hine. **130, 132, 133–154** Rosario Valderrama. **163, 184** Sherri Haab. **191** Mircea Catusanu. **217** Lizi Boyd.